D. C. Thomson & Co. Ltd. GLASGOW, LONDON, DUNDEE.

£1·80

OOR WULLIE

Who thinks that soap is nasty stuff—
Tae " wash " yer hands, a towel's enough . . ?

That's Wullie!

Who leaves footprints in wet cement
As off he goes on mischief bent . . ?

That's Wullie!

Who leaves the seat o' his best breeks
Snagged on the wire as fun he seeks . .?

That's Wullie!

A muddy ba', a snow-white sheet,
A mighty kick, then swift retreat . . .

That's Wullie!

Whose jaws work overtime when he
Sees what his Ma has baked for tea . . ?

Wullie!

And who, when it's time tae mak' ye laugh,
Does it all a treat, no' half . . ?

OOR WULLIE

Printed and Published in Great Britain by D. C. THOMSON & CO., LTD., 185 Fleet Street, London EC4A 2HS.
© D. C. THOMSON & CO., LTD., 1984.
ISBN 0 85116 320 3

His itchy back makes things go wrong—

But he's " tickled " pink before too long!

It's easy to tell—

That Wullie can't spell!

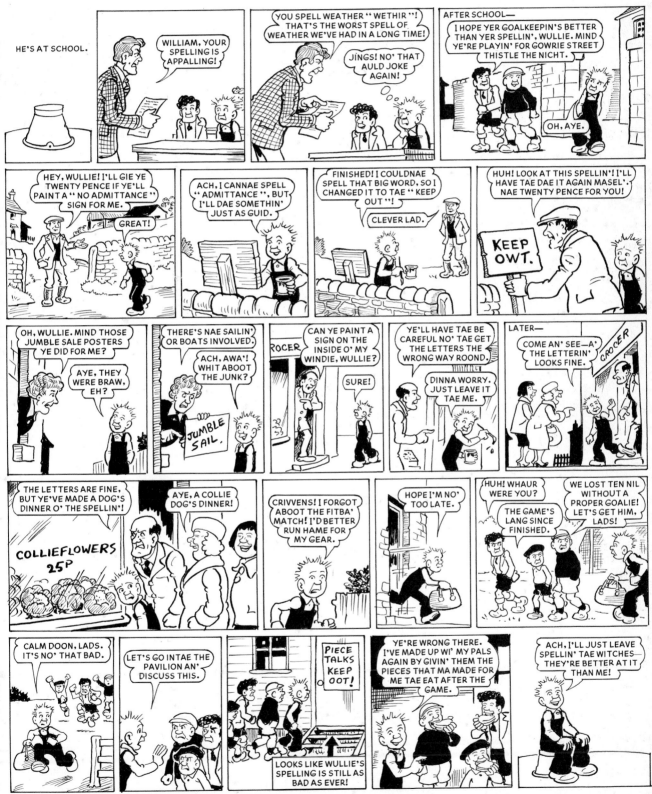

There's trouble for you-know-who—

On a bicycle built for two!

A BIG let-down—

From Jingo the clown!

This new lad knows all the tricks—

But see Wull land him in a fix!

Wull does his best to guard that box—

But in the end, it gives him shocks.

Your face will fill with laughter creases—

When Wull's pals do their party pieces!

This hat's a handy thing indeed—

It's everywhere, 'cept on his heid!

There's danger on the Whinny Braes—

Or so oor climbing hero says!

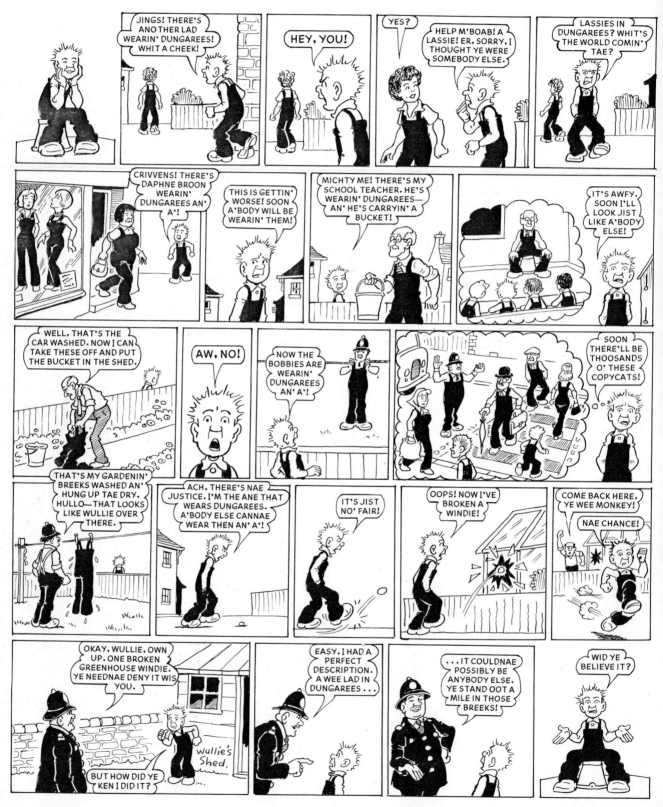

. . . but in the end, wee Wull believes—

The fortune told in his tea leaves!

HE'LL BE HAME FOR HIS DINNER SOON.

I'M HAME, MA! OH, HELLO, MRS McNAB.

HELLO, WULLIE.

LATER— MRS McNAB WILL READ YER CUP AFORE YE GO BACK TAE SCHOOL, WULLIE. SHE CAN TELL YER FORTUNE, YE KEN.

A'RICHT!

I SEE YOUR FUTURE INVOLVING MANY LINES. THEY ARE GOING TO MAKE YOU VERY UNHAPPY.

REALLY?

CHEERIO, THEN. I'M OFF TAE SCHOOL.

FORTUNE TELLING—WHIT A LOAD O' JUNK!

HUH! LINES WILL MAK' ME UNHAPPY, EH? THERE'S BILL DOW WI' A FISHIN' LINE. THAT'LL NO' MAK' ME SAD.

HI, WULLIE. LIKE TAE TRY OOT MY NEW ROD?

SURE, BILL.

JINGS! THAT'S A WHOPPER!

AYE, IT'S A CRACKER!

'BYE, BILL.

WELL, THAT DIDNAE MAK' ME UNHAPPY.

HOW ABOOT LETTIN' ME PAINT SOME O' YER LINES, MR MACKAY?

I'D BE GLAD IF YE COULD, WULLIE, I'M FAIR PUGGLED.

THIS IS NO' MAKIN' ME UNHAPPY.

'BYE, MR MACKAY!

THANKS FOR YER HELP, WULLIE.

HEY, WULLIE! FANCY TAKIN' THE ENGINE UP THE LINE? THE INSPECTOR'S OFF TODAY.

GREAT!

YER WEE SCENIC RAILWAY IS JIST BRAW, MR ELLIS.

THANKS, I'D BETTER AWA' TAE SCHOOL NOW.

WELL, THE RAILWAY LINE DIDNAE MAK' ME UNHAPPY.

CRIVVENS! LOOK AT THE TIME! I'M AWFY LATE!

YOU'RE LATE AGAIN, WILLIAM. I'M GOING TO PUNISH YOU . . .

MICHTY ME. THIS'LL BE THE LINES MRS McNAB WIS ON ABOOT.

. . . BUT YOU'LL BE PUNISHED IN A NEW WAY. GO TO MISS MACLEOD'S CLASS AND HELP OUT THERE THIS AFTERNOON.

MISS MACLEOD TEACHES DOMESTIC SCIENCE. I'LL LIKELY GET TAE TEST THEIR BAKIN' AN' A'THING. MRS McNAB WIS WRONG!

IN TROUBLE AGAIN, WILLIAM? GO AND HELP THE GIRLS OVER THERE.

AW, NO!

A WASHIN' LINE!

HUH! I'M GOIN' TAE INSIST ON TEA BAGS IN FUTURE!

Well, well, well, ye'll never guess—

What goes wi' Wull, tae Auntie Bess!

Wullie's latest ploy's just great—

Till he's joined by a heavyweight!

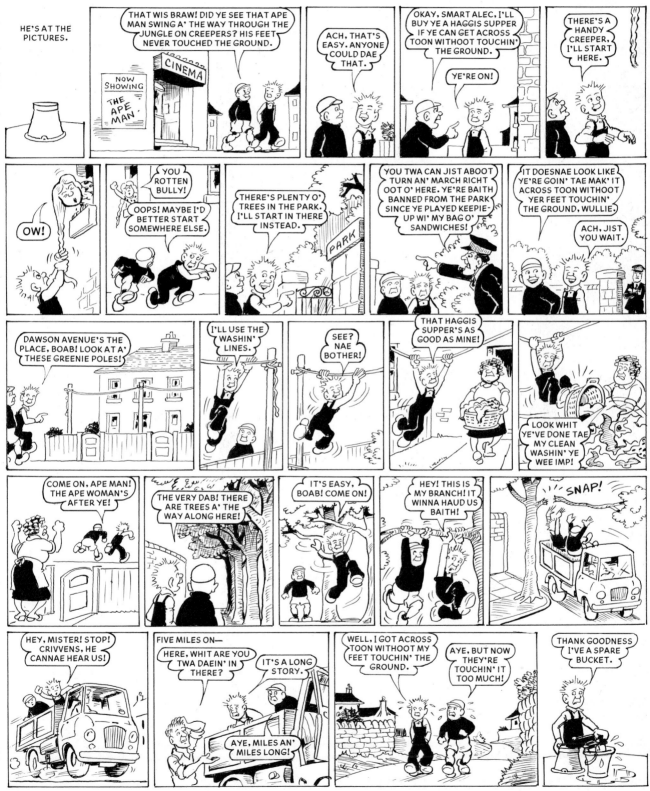

When it comes to planning fun—
Two heads are better than just one!

Now Oor Wullie's seeking fame—

As " big boss " in the boxing game!

Oor Wullie's got a super plan—

To build himself a " cartie-van "!

It's half-past twelve. " Come on!" Wull cries—

And cuts a boaster doon tae size!

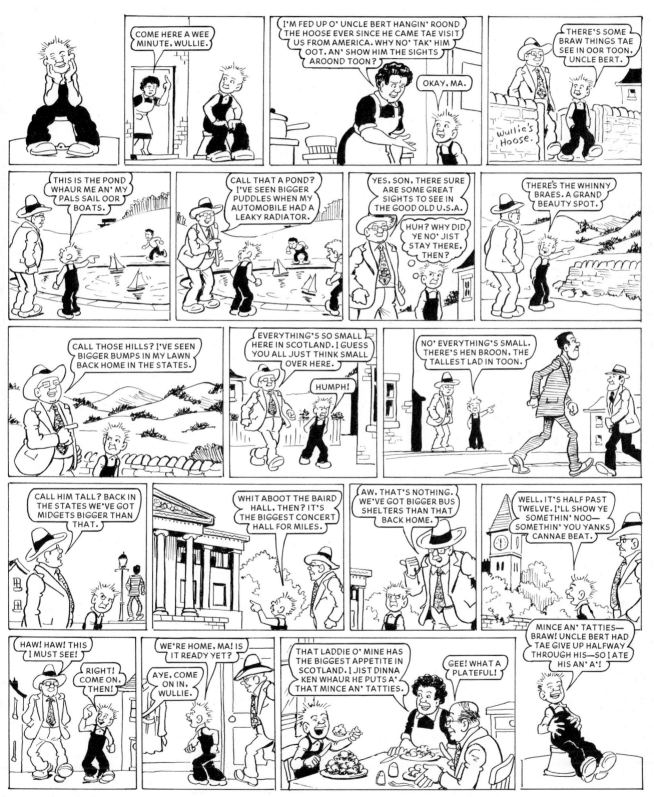

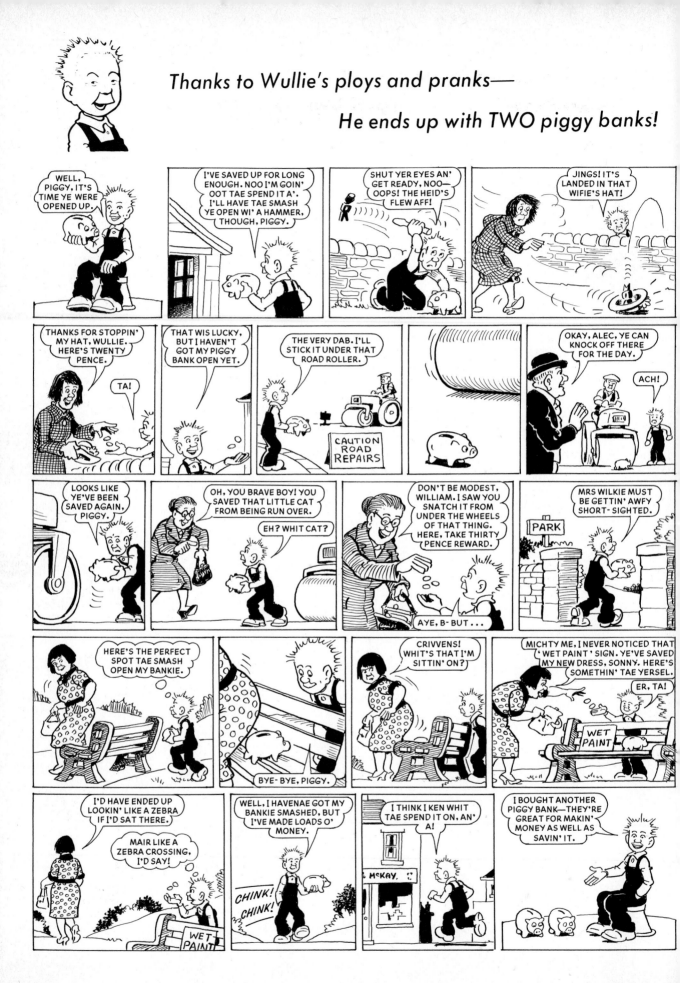

See Soapy chuckle loud and long—

When Wullie gets his clues all wrong!

Clean boots, pressed breeks, all spick and span—
Now spot Oor Wullie, if you can!

Wull's dancing lessons come up trumps—

When he learns ballet jumps!

Wullie does a lot o' frettin'—

Until he sees what Murdoch's gettin!

Wull's never lonely, never glum—

Thanks to his ever-present chum!

Oor Wullie's quick with words, and how—

His big fat chum is FLAT Bob now!

Four times Murdoch's hat's sent flyin'—

And Wullie isn't even tryin'!

It's the funniest thing yet—

When he tracks doon this pet!

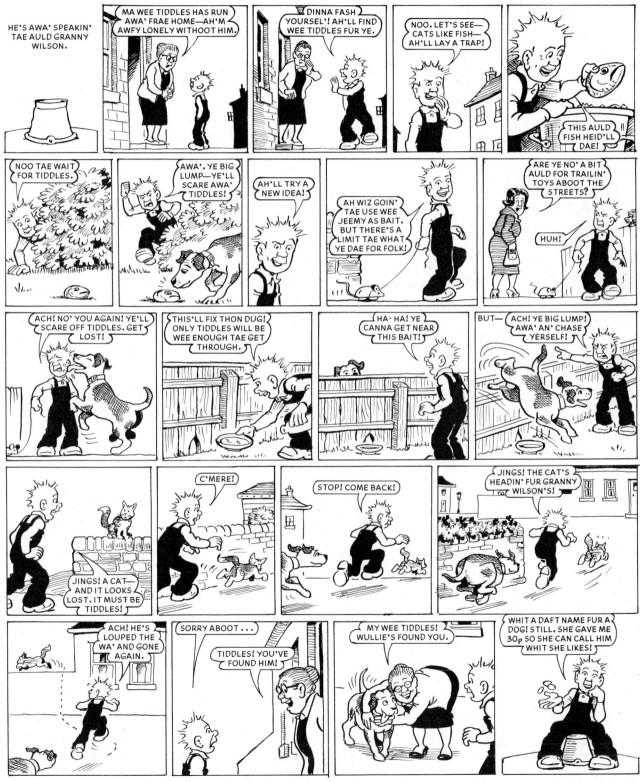

See the scarf that Wullie's got—

And then see how it keeps him hot!

When everything is said and done—

No one's a " patch " on Wull for fun!

Some smart replies—

Then a big surprise!

Things don't go quite as Wullie planned—

So see how his Pa " lends a hand "!

Oor Wullie may be good at " chessies "—

But he's a flop at writing essays!

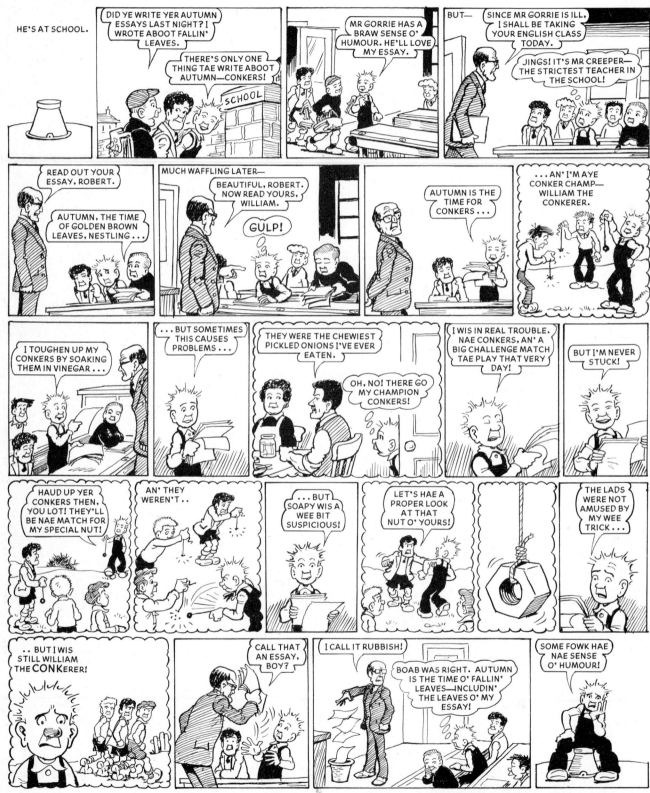

Cups of every shape and size—

But will Wull EVER win a prize?

A box o' chalks—

Brings Wullie shocks!

All Wullie's hopes go sadly wrong—

Some queues are best when they are long!

You'll no' half goggle when you look—

At the title o' Wull's library book!

Poor Oor Wullie comes off worst—

When the lads' new ba' is burst!

Eck's got a moothie, there's a fiddle and a drum—

And the orchestra leader's your funny wee chum!

There's a real how-d'ye-do—

At Wullie's wee zoo!

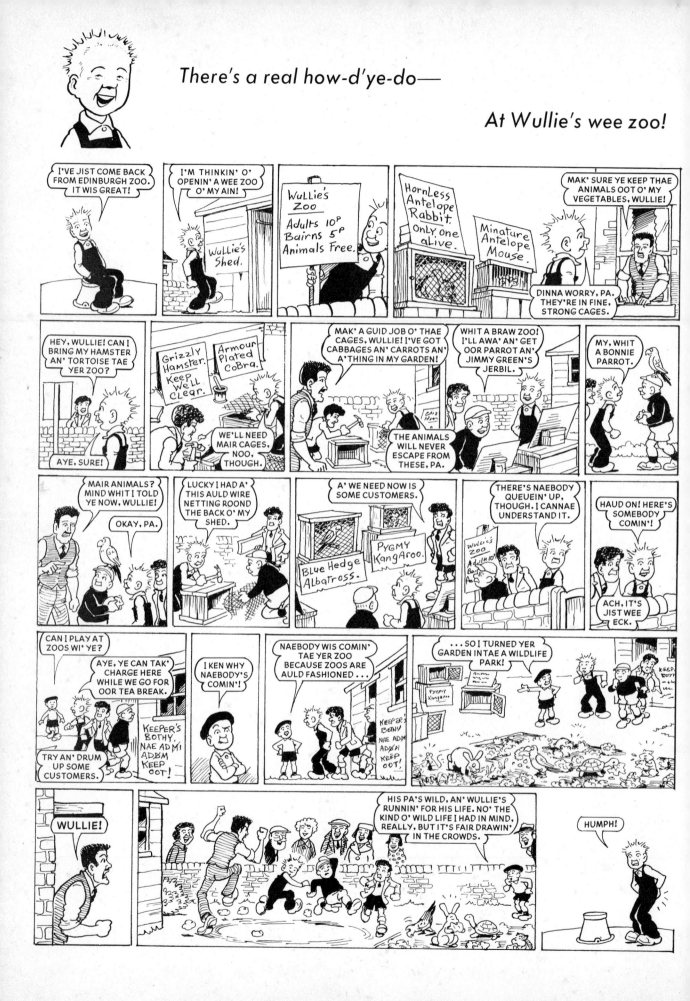

See the look on this 'tec's face—

When he helps Murdoch " crack a case "!

Though Tiny Terrors be their name—

They're mighty big lads, just the same!

He disna half get up tae capers—

When he goes oot, deliverin' papers!

Just see the perils Wullie meets—

As he goes struggling doon the streets!

On history, Wull's really keen—

Till he comes to the battle scene!

Wull's cowboy talk—

Gives Ma a shock!

Sandy's super swimming gear—

Comes in really handy here!

Things are lookin' up this summer—

Oor Wullie's goin' tae be a "plummer"!

Some folk think gardening keeps you fit—

But Wull can't see the " point " of it!

Wull's oot tae see the fitba', free—

Up high on stilts, or in a tree!

Will Wullie's wellies leak or no'?—

That's what oor laddie wants tae know!

Though through the toon Oor Wullie flies—
It seems he needs MORE exercise!

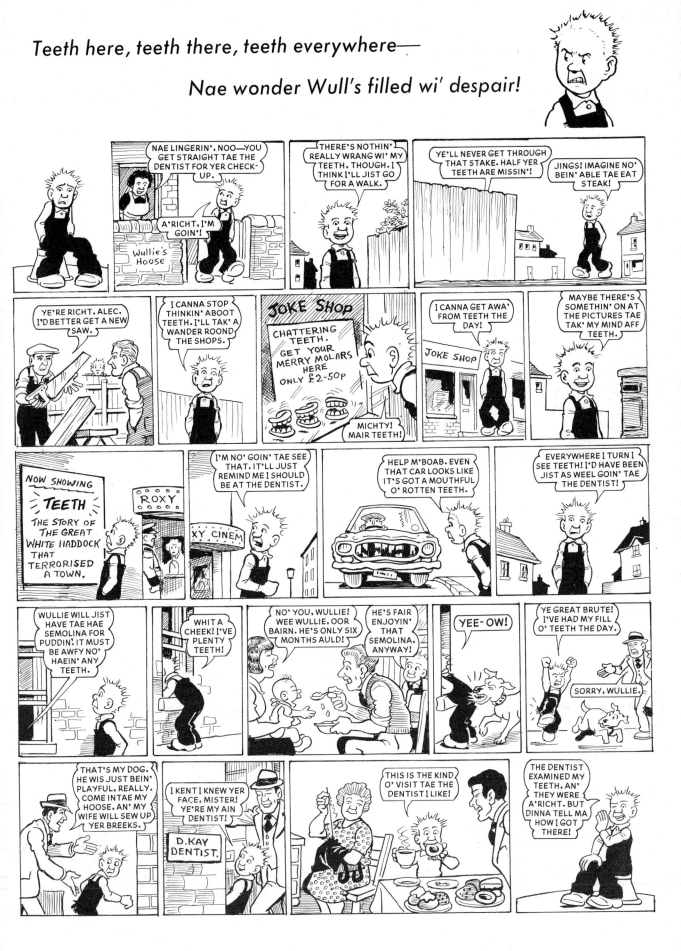

After keeping things so quiet—

Oor lad would sleep right through a riot!

Oor Wull gets in a proper tizz—

Just trying to find what time it is!

Archie Ologist? Who's he?—

Just tak' a look below and see!

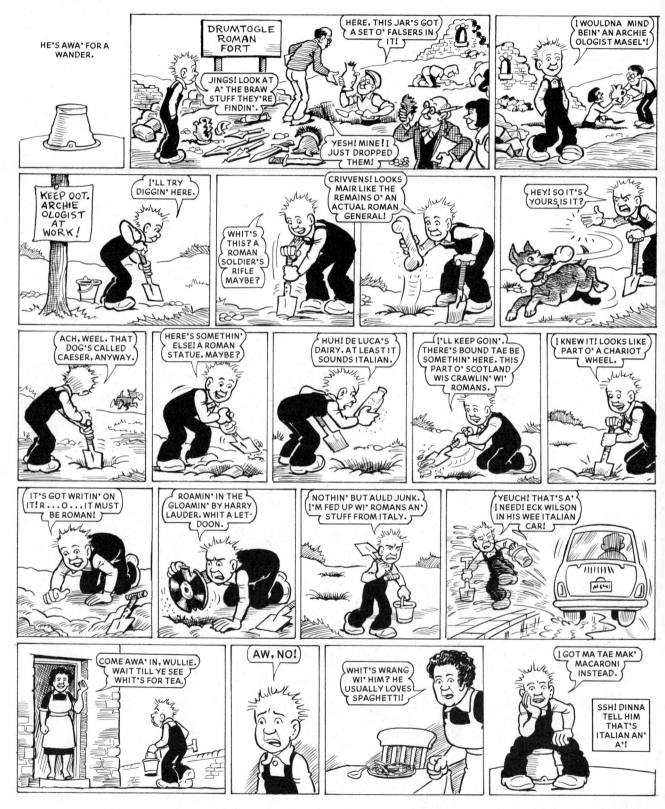

Beware Oor Wullie's Leisure Centre—

There are shocks galore for all who enter!

Why that medal? Ah, that's the question—
Of all the answers, Wull's is the best yin!

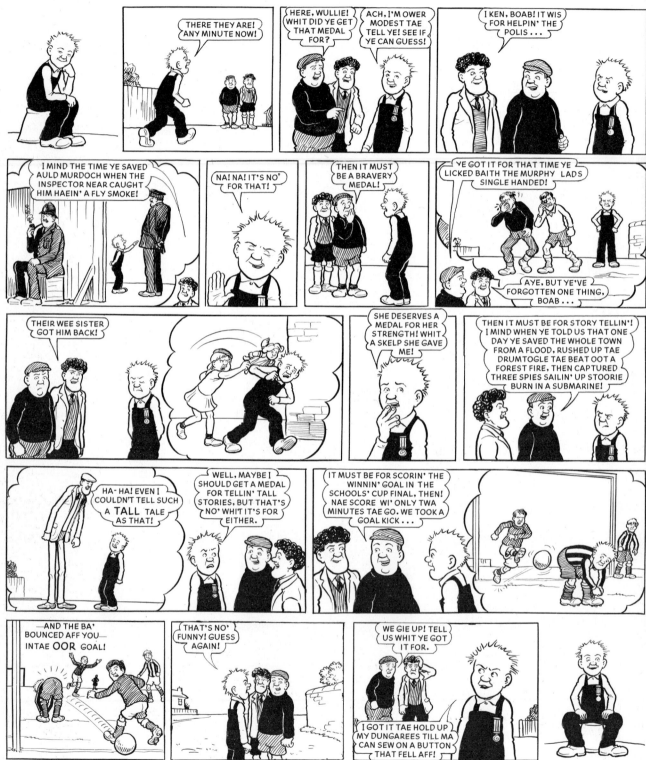

You'll soon see why Oor Wullie's glum—

Wee Jeemy is a DEAR wee chum!

A bath for Wullie? Not a chance—

He leads his Ma a merry dance!

Wull does his best to save these pies—

But he still gets a big surprise!

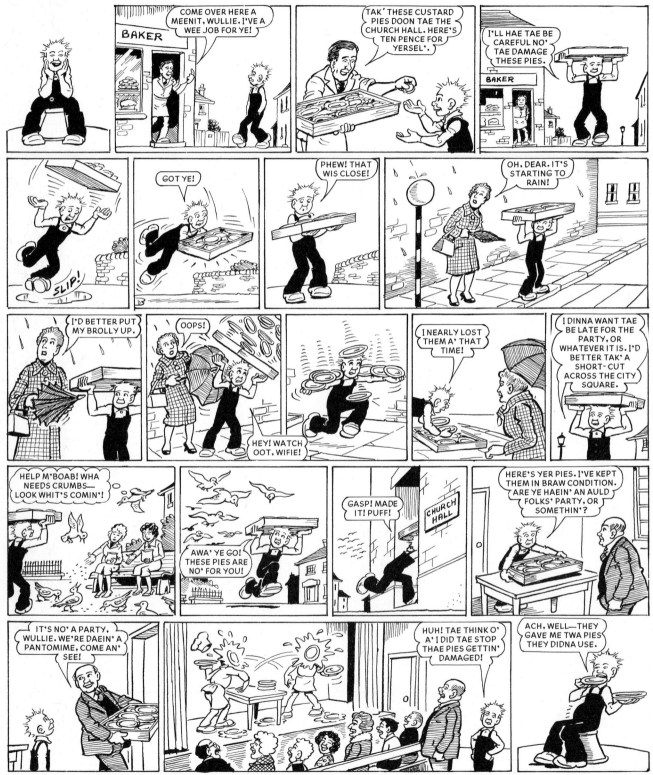

Puir wee Wull. His luck is oot—

See his footwear get the boot!

A sanctuary for birds? That's grand!—

But things don't go quite as Wull planned.

Just when it seems disaster looms—

Up come Wullie's quick-grow blooms!

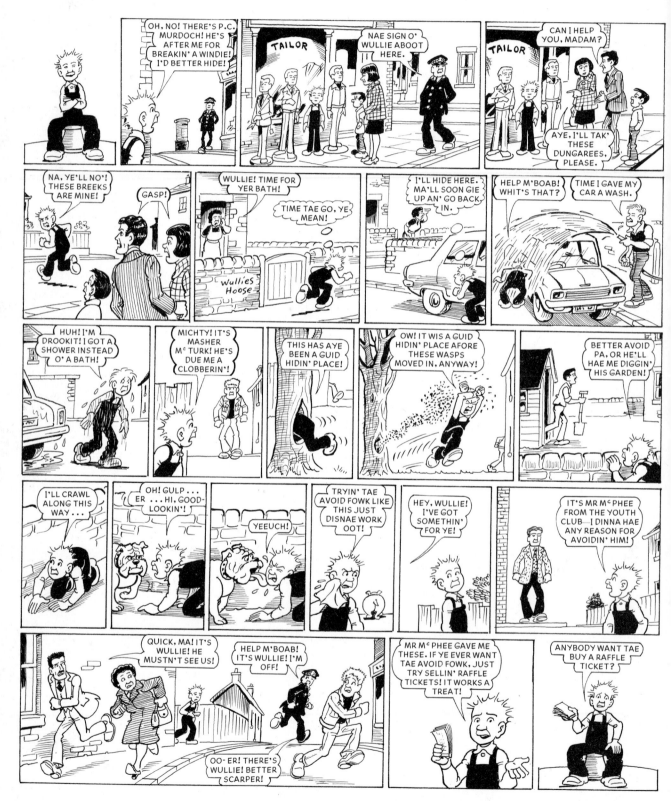

. . . but no one wants to listen to—

The only lad whose story's true!

Whit a din! Whit a racket!—

And guess what's inside that big packet!

The folk line up for Wull's coach trip—

And sure enough, he gets a tip!

With just one catch—

He's the man o' the match!

All Oor Wullie wants to know—

Is what made Hen Broon grow and grow!

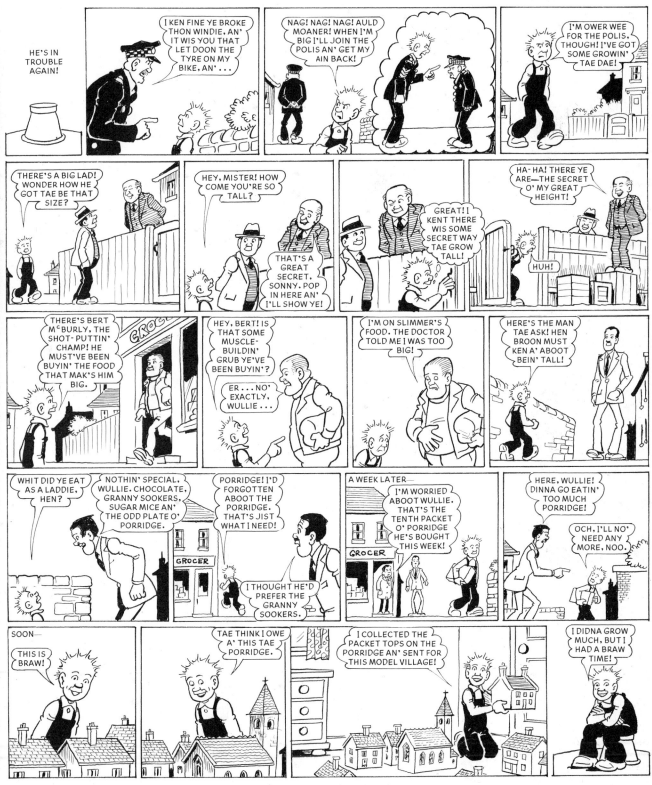

There's good reason for Wull's frowns—

Life's got too many UPS and downs!

Oor Wullie's smart. Trust him to find—

Auld comics of a different kind!

Oor lad provides big smiles all round—

Until Jacques' missing " pal " is found!

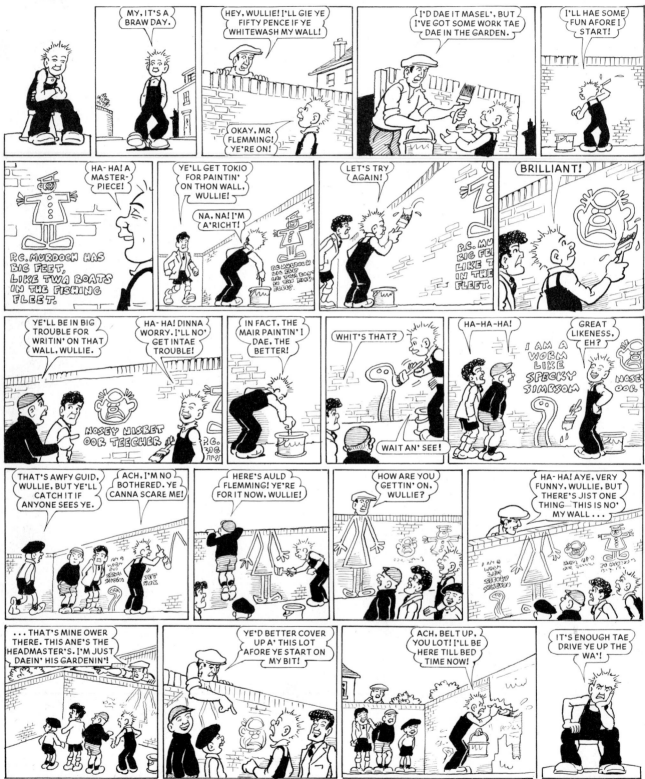

Wull's paintings may well be disasters—

But they all sell, just like Old Masters!

Oor Wullie comes a proper cropper—
His essay sounds like one big " whopper "!

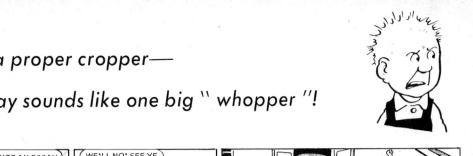

All Wullie's ploys go sadly wrong—

Until his uncle comes along.

Oor Wullie's life is never borin'—

Here he is, awa' explorin'!

Pets are troublesome, no' half—

Just see Wull's " enormouse " laugh!

Michty me, just tak' a look—

Here's Wull the waiter, Bob the cook!

Oor Wullie's shopping list's so long—
He's guaranteed to get it wrong!

Here's a special snowball fight—

Trust oor lad to do things "write"!

See that big smile on Ma's face—

She's got the perfect hiding-place!